Aardman

Wallace & Gromit

Gromit

IT'S A DOG'S LIFE

with Gromit

EGMONT

We bring stories to life

First published in Great Britain 2008
by Egmont UK Limited
239 Kensington High Street, London W8 6SA

Text by Anna Bowles
Design by Claire Hammond

ISBN 978 1 4052 3811 3
1 3 5 7 9 10 8 6 4 2

Printed in Malaysia

Aardman

Wallace & Gromit

Gromit

IT'S A DOG'S LIFE

with Gromit

EGMONT

Don't be afraid to face your troubles head on.

It's always jam tomorrow . . . but don't forget to savour your cornflakes today.

Relaxing with a good book can keep you from blowing a fuse.

There's no shame in taking a supporting role at times.

Tea makes (almost) anything better.

You may feel low
sometimes – but you'll
bounce back!

There are worse things than having egg on your face.

Have faith, and
an answer may drop
into your lap.

Read up on your problems. But take action before they grow too big to manage.

Try not to be jealous.
A true friend will come
back to you in the end.

Don't be thrown by the occasional crisis.

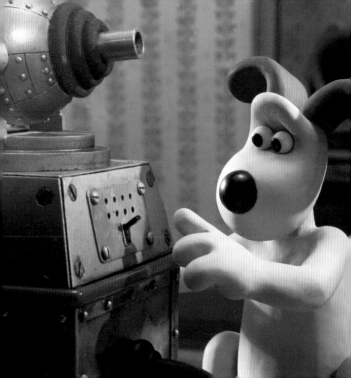

Don't be afraid
to experiment.

EVENING POST

GROMIT GETS LIFE

RUSTLING
RASCAL
TO DO
PORRIDGE

Hopes of an end to

EVERY DAY

Cash in now
YOU could

Good friends will flock
to your aid in a crisis.

Never let life give you the cold shoulder!

Don't let bad manners
bring you down.

TO A DEAR
DOG

It's the thought
that counts.

If you can keep your
head while all about
you are losing theirs,
you are probably a
dog who can't speak.

A good nosh can make
you feel much better.

Violence solves nothing. One of Gromit's looks can do the job instead.

Whatever your job,
take pride.

Keep your eyes open for a route out of trouble.

Go easy on the caffeine
or you won't sleep.

Make the most of time that would otherwise be wasted.

Join in a friend's pastimes – even if you think they are cheesy.

**If you're down,
a friend's enthusiasm
can be catching.**

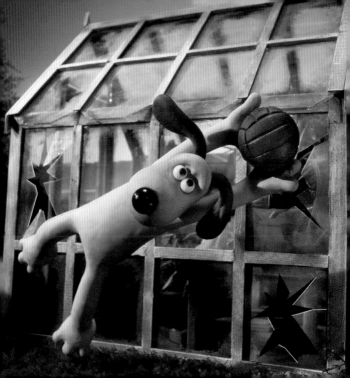

Deal with one thing
at a time. If you miss
a few, you can clear
up afterwards.

Good things come to those who wait.

Don't get burdened with an unfair amount of responsibility.

The ancient art
of tae kwon dog helps
Gromit maintain
a mystical calm.

Smile! It may never happen.